Lift Little Voices

Songs and Musical Games
for Young Children

Deborah Carter
Carol Greene

CPH
SAINT LOUIS

For the Emmanuel Cherubs, past, present, and future

Contents

Introduction

Songs that Praise God

Hello and Good-bye Songs

Seasonal Songs and Activities

Songs and Activities that Teach Music Theory

Special Songs

Seasonal Index

Title Index

Introduction

If you work with small children, you know that getting them to lift little voices is scarcely a problem. (Getting them to lower them—well—that's something else.)

Encouraging the youngest singers to lift their voices in song to God is not difficult either. Young children seem to feel an urge to pray and praise deep inside them and are quite willing to let it out. Their earnestness and fervor are often more moving to the adults listening than the actual music they make.

But there's no reason you can't have both fervor and music. Following are some time-tested principles for incorporating a lively use of music in your early childhood classroom, or choir rehearsals with small children; a collection of new songs with teaching tips; and games and activities to foster musical growth in any Christian setting.

Whether you direct a choir of young children or want to include music time in your early childhood curriculum, it is wise to recruit some people to help you. A pianist can be a real blessing. It's difficult to play and engage children's attention at the same time. Other helpers (older children or retired persons) can pass out craft materials and snacks and help maintain discipline and supervise visits to the bathroom. Ask these folks to take an active part in the program—dancing, singing, playing, and doing activities with the children. You can bet that they'll get caught up in the fun.

Sitting in a circle on the floor is a good music setup for small children. Use masking tape ×'s or stick-on dots to indicate where each child should sit. If you need to move the children from one room or area to another, arrange the children in "trains" with your helpers as the "engines."

One of the most important things to remember when planning music time with little ones is flexibility within structure. If you are directing a choir, develop a simple format to follow at each meeting. This can be as simple as starting with a hello song and ending with a good-bye song and treats.

Allow yourself the freedom to switch gears as necessary. If it's raining and the children are restless, change your quiet activity to a more physical one. Move from one activity to another fairly quickly, keeping a balance between physical and mental activities. If you direct a choir, total rehearsal time should be no longer than 45 minutes, including games and snacks.

Keep children actively participating with you rather than listening passively. Ask them to imitate your hand motions as you teach lyrics. Let them act out stories as you tell them. Don't talk about a song for five minutes—lead them in singing it with you. Have them dance to a melody as they learn it. (Dances that get progressively faster are always big hits.) As you teach the children to follow your direction, hold fermatas ridiculously long and let them watch you like eagles for your cut-off.

Set up a display area for attendance charts and schedules and for displaying children's artwork. If you don't have a bulletin board, string a clothesline and hang children's work with clothespins.

You do not need to mimic the technique of a Toscanini to conduct small children. Keep your direction simple. If you are conducting very small children in church, sit or kneel before them and encourage them to watch you mouth the words.

Be happy and upbeat as you work with little singers. Together you're participating in one of God's great gifts—music. You become one with all the saints and angels praising Him for the gift of His Son. Enjoy yourselves!

The People of Israel

C. G.

Carol Greene

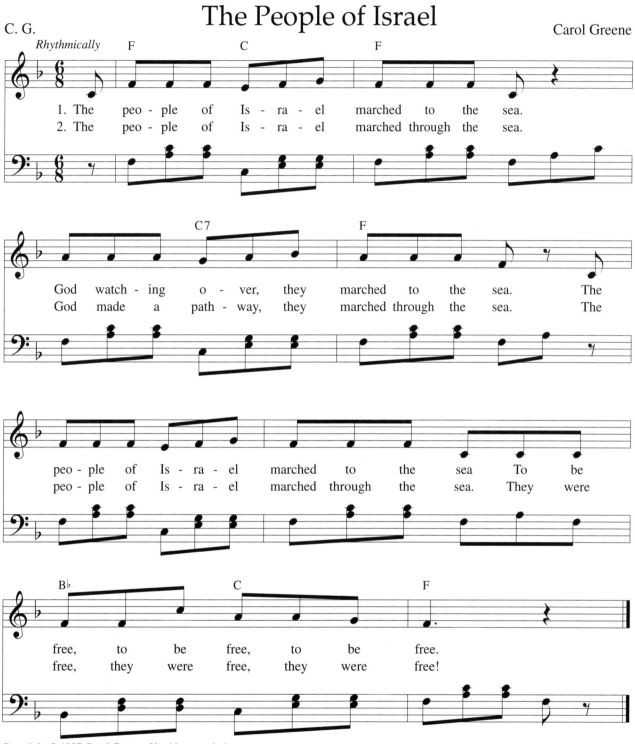

Rhythmically

1. The peo-ple of Is-ra-el marched to the sea.
2. The peo-ple of Is-ra-el marched through the sea.

God watch-ing o-ver, they marched to the sea. The
God made a path-way, they marched through the sea. The

peo-ple of Is-ra-el marched to the sea To be
peo-ple of Is-ra-el marched through the sea. They were

free, to be free, to be free.
free, they were free, they were free!

Tell the children a simple version of the story of the Exodus as you teach this song. Divide the children into two groups. Group 1 can be the sea and step apart so group 2 can walk through. Then switch roles.

God Made It Rain

C. G.

Carol Greene

Tap a pencil on something made of tin or tip a rain stick each time the word "rain" occurs. Let children take turns making the rain sounds. They will also enjoy saying the word "drip" on each quarter rest.

8

Listen to the Stories

C. G.

Carol Greene

You won't want to teach all the stanzas of this song at once. Teach a stanza to go with a specific Bible story, or choose two or three stanzas to learn in a religion lesson about trusting God.

God Made a Promise

Carol Greene

W. A. Mozart (adapted)

Allegretto

A♭   B♭m

1. God___ made a prom - ise long a - go, A___
2. We are wait - ing, wait - ing long for the Child. We are

E♭   A♭

spe - cial prom - ise long a - go, A___ Christ - mas prom - ise
wait - ing for the spe - cial Child. We are wait - ing for the

B♭m   E♭   A♭

long a - go. God will keep His prom - ise too.
Christ - mas Child. God will keep His prom - ise too.

Ask an older child or adult to play the melody on bells, either as the children sing or as an interlude between stanzas.

What Do You Hear

C. G.

Carol Greene

Children will enjoy acting out Mary singing and the donkey clopping. They might spread their arms or even spin around to indicate "the whole world."

11

Glory to God

C. G.

Carol Greene

12

Children especially enjoy clapping on the refrain of this song. Help them observe the rests in the stanzas by moving your finger rhythmically to your lips at each rest.

Sleep Now, Baby

C. G.

Carol Greene

1. Sleep now, Ba - by, lit - tle Lord Je - sus.
Last stanza: Sleep now, Ba - by, lit - tle Lord Je - sus.

Sleep now, Ba - by. Don't you cry. Sleep now, Ba - by,
Sleep now, Ba - by. Don't you cry. Sleep now, Ba - by,

lit - tle Lord Je - sus. Mar - y sings a lull - a - by.
lit - tle Lord Je - sus. We all sing a lull - a - by.

Copyright © 1997 Carol Greene. Used by permission.

Make up new stanzas to this song by asking the children to fill in other characters from the Christmas story in the last phrase. "Joseph sings a lullaby," "Angels sing a lullaby," and so on.

13

Ring the Bells

Carol Greene

Ring the bells! Beat the drum!

Clap your hands! The Ba - by's come!

What lit - tle Ba - by? Lit - tle ba - by Je - sus! What lit - tle Ba - by? God's own Son!

Da capo to second ending.

14

Children will enjoy using rhythm instruments with this song. For a performance you might want older children to play bells with you.

Glory Alleluia

C. G.

Carol Greene

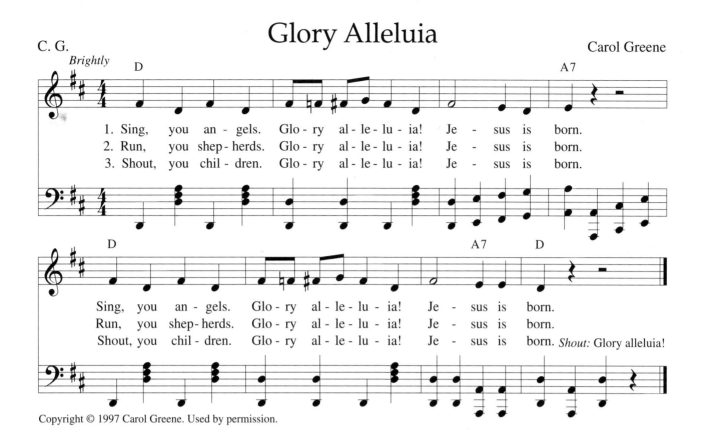

1. Sing, you an - gels. Glo - ry al - le - lu - ia! Je - sus is born.
2. Run, you shep - herds. Glo - ry al - le - lu - ia! Je - sus is born.
3. Shout, you chil - dren. Glo - ry al - le - lu - ia! Je - sus is born.

Sing, you an - gels. Glo - ry al - le - lu - ia! Je - sus is born.
Run, you shep - herds. Glo - ry al - le - lu - ia! Je - sus is born.
Shout, you chil - dren. Glo - ry al - le - lu - ia! Je - sus is born. *Shout:* Glory alleluia!

Let the children play percussion instruments as you sing this song.

15

Bright Angels Sing

C. G.

Carol Greene

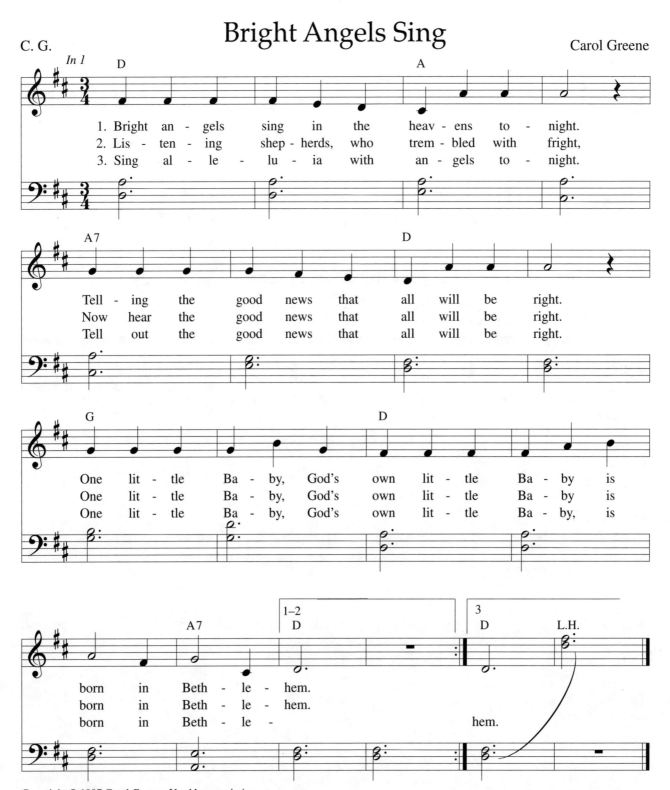

1. Bright an - gels sing in the heav - ens to - night.
2. Lis - ten - ing shep - herds, who trem - bled with fright,
3. Sing al - le - lu - ia with an - gels to - night.

Tell - ing the good news that all will be right.
Now hear the good news that all will be right.
Tell out the good news that all will be right.

One lit - tle Ba - by, God's own lit - tle Ba - by is
One lit - tle Ba - by, God's own lit - tle Ba - by is
One lit - tle Ba - by, God's own lit - tle Ba - by, is

born in Beth - le - hem.
born in Beth - le - hem.
born in Beth - le - hem.

Children will enjoy acting out the angels' visit to the shepherds as they sing this song. To dress up this song a bit as an anthem, you might have older children play the bass line or chords on bells as an accompaniment.

Jesus, Our Star

C. G.

Carol Greene

Explain that Jesus is the bright light that leads us to heaven. Children will enjoy marching behind a leader carrying a star attached to a stick as they sing. Then they may decorate stars to hang from the ceiling.

If I Were a Camel

C. G.

Carol Greene

1. If I were a cam - el, a cam - el, a cam - el, I'd carry a wise man to Beth - le - hem.
2. If I were a bright star, a bright star, a bright star, I'd shine all the night o - ver Beth - le - hem.
3. But I can do some - thing, do some - thing, do some - thing, I'll sing for the Christ child at Beth - le - hem.

18

Help children make up actions to be a camel and a star. Have them substitute other things they would like to do for Jesus for the word "sing" in stanza 3.

Bright Star Shining

C. G.

Carol Greene

Lyrics:

1. Bright star shin - ing in the Beth - le'm sky,
2. Bright star shin - ing on a low - ly place,
3. Bright star shin - ing in our hearts to - day,

East - ern stran - gers came a - rid - ing by,
Stran - gers gaz - ing on a lit - tle face,
Bring some stran - ger to the Sav - ior's way,

Wea - ry cam - el blinks a blear - y eye:
Feel their hearts fill up with heav'n - ly grace:
Let the light that's shin - ing in you say,

Look - ing for the Son of God.
They have found the Son of God.
"Come now to the Son of God."

Encourage the children to clap and sing this song as a lively spiritual. It's also a good text to act out. Help the children think of ways they can lead others to Jesus.

19

Blest Are We

A. M. R.

Ann Marie Ruhlin

1. Blest are we when we share. Blest are we when we care.
2. Blest are we when we're sad. Blest are we when we're glad.

Blest are we___ here and there be - cause we love our God.
Peace and joy are what we have be - cause we love our God.

Refrain

Love our God and neigh - bor too, Think of them, me and you,

Do the best that we can do be - cause we love our God.

Tell the children in a simple way about Jesus' Beatitudes as you teach this song.

20

God Cares for You

C. G.

Carol Greene

Cheerfully

1. Don't be a - fraid. Don't be up -
2. Look at the birds. Look at up the

set. God will pro - vide.
flow - ers. God sends them food.

God won't for - get. God cares for
God sends them show - ers. God cares for

you. God cares for you.
them. God cares for you.

Help the children act out this song. They can point to one another on the words "God cares for you." Explain the word "provide"—God gives us everything we need, even the gift of His Son to win us life with Him.

Float, Little Boat

C. G.

Carol Greene

Moderato

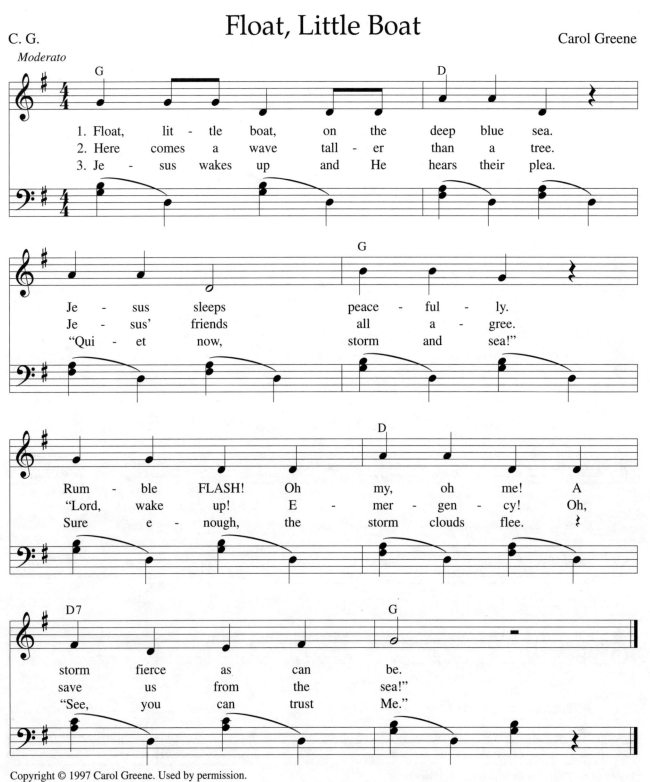

1. Float, lit - tle boat, on the deep blue sea.
2. Here comes a wave tall - er than a tree.
3. Je - sus wakes up and He hears their plea.

Je - sus sleeps peace - ful - ly.
Je - sus' friends all a - gree.
"Qui - et now, storm and sea!"

Rum - ble FLASH! Oh my, oh me! A
"Lord, wake up! E - mer - gen - cy! Oh,
Sure e - nough, the storm clouds flee.

storm fierce as can be.
save us from the sea!"
"See, you can trust Me."

Tell children the story of Jesus stilling the storm. Have them act out the story as they sing the song.

Walking, Walking to See Jesus

C. G.

Carol Greene

1. Walk-ing, walk-ing to see Je-sus, Lit-tle chil-dren laugh and
no! You can't see Je-sus," His dis - ci - ples stern - ly
wel-come, lit-tle chil-dren," Je - sus says. "Come, it is

sing. "Will He hug us? Will He bless us? He is Lord of ev - 'ry
say. "He must rest. We don't want chil-dren Both-er - ing the Lord to -
fine. I will hug you. I will bless you. Lit - tle chil-dren, you are

thing."
day."
Mine."

2. "No, no,
3. "Wel - come,

Tell the story of Jesus blessing the children as you teach this song. Ask adult helpers to act out the parts of adults and children the parts of children as you sing.

With Faith as Big as a Mustard Seed

C. G.

Carol Greene

1. With faith as big as a mus - tard seed (This is what the Lord Je - sus once said.), You can tell a moun - tain, "Get out of here And move some - place else in - stead."

2. With faith as big as a mus - tard seed, You can say to a mul - ber - ry tree, "Now pick up your roots from the ground, my friend, And plant your - self in the sea."

3. A mus - tard seed is a ti - ny thing When the farm - er puts it in the ground But it grows in - to a fine tree with room for birds to perch all a - round.

Refrain

With faith as big as a mus - tard seed, A tee - ny ti - ny, it - ty bit - ty mus - tard seed, With faith as big as a mus - tard seed, You can do great things.

24

Show the children a mustard seed or draw a dot on a piece of paper and say, "This is how tiny a mustard seed is!" Children will enjoy acting out the stanzas.

The Good Shepherd

Carol Greene

Johannes Brahms, adapted

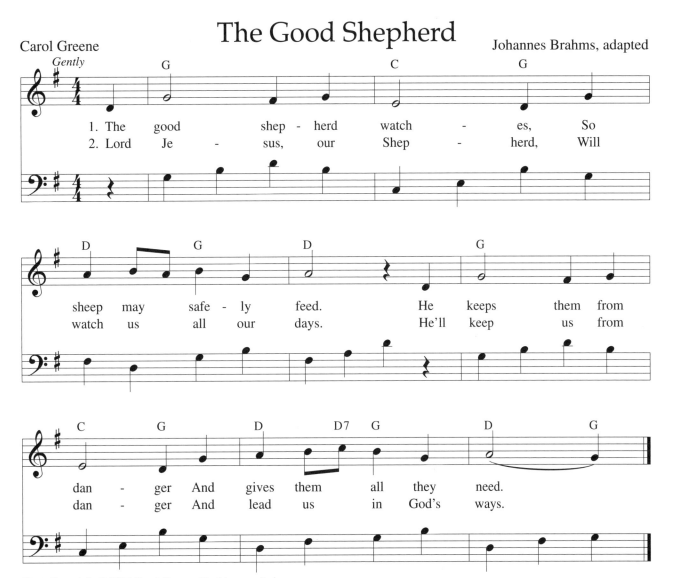

1. The good shep - herd watch - es, So
2. Lord Je - sus, our Shep - herd, Will

sheep may safe - ly feed. He keeps them from
watch us all our days. He'll keep us from

dan - ger And gives them all they need.
dan - ger And lead us in God's ways.

Pretend to be a shepherd and lead the children as your sheep. "Come over here, little sheep. Here's some really good grass to eat. Oh, oh! There's a bear! Get out of here, you bear!" Explain that Jesus lovingly protects us as His little lambs and gives us everything we need.

25

March On, Little Donkey

C. G.

Carol Greene

1. March on, lit - tle don - key, and car - ry the
2. Shout out, all you peo - ple, and wor - ship the
3. Sing out, lit - tle chil - dren, and wel - come the

Lord. March on, lit - tle don - key, and car - ry the
Lord. Shout out, all you peo - ple, and wor - ship the
Lord. Sing out, lit - tle chil - dren, and wel - come the

Lord. March on, lit - tle don - key, and car - ry the
Lord. Shout out, all you peo - ple, and wor - ship the
Lord. Sing out, lit - tle chil - dren, and wel - come the

Lord, Go - ing to Je - ru - sa - lem.
Lord, Go - ing to Je - ru - sa - lem.
Lord, Go - ing to Je - ru - sa - lem.

Let the children march to this song and wave green crepe paper streamers as they sing. They will also enjoy sitting on the floor and making clopping noises by hitting the floor or their knees with open palms.

26

Glory, Glory, Lord Jesus

C. G.

Carol Greene

You and your children can express a lot of joy with this song. Encourage children to clap on beat 1 of each measure and smile as they sing.

27

Jesus Is Risen

C. G.

Carol Greene

Je-sus is ris-en Out of death's pris-on.
Shout it and say it. Sing it and play it.

Tell all the world that the Lord is a-live.
Tell all the world that the Lord is a-

live. Oh, tell all the world that the Lord is a-

live. Oh, tell all the world that the Lord is a-live!

28

Show the children how to sing each "tell all the world" phrase in the second ending with more volume.

Jesus Lives! Alleluia, Amen!

C. G.

Carol Greene

1. Je - sus lives! Al - le - lu - ia, a - men! We will sing it a - gain and a -
lives! Al - le - lu - ia, a - men! We will sing it a - gain and a -

gain To the earth, to the sky, Way down low, way up high. Je - sus
gain, Ev - 'ry girl, ev - 'ry boy, With our hearts full of joy. Je - sus

lives! Al - le - lu - ia, a - men! 2. Je - sus
lives! Al - le - lu - ia, a - men! Je - sus

lives! Al - le - lu - ia, a - men! Je - sus lives! Al - le - lu - ia, a - men!

Help the children develop motions for this song. They will enjoy shouting the final "amen" rather than singing it.

Thank God, Alleluia

C. G.

Carol Greene

1. For gifts from the earth,____ For gifts from a - bove, For
2. For sun - shine and snow - flakes, For an - i - mals too, For

peo - ple who love us, And peo - ple we love: Thank God, al - le -
lov - ing us al - ways, Dear God, we thank You.

lu - ia! Thank God, al - le - lu - ia! Thank God, al - le - lu - ia, a -

men! A - men!

30 This is a good song to dance to, especially during the interlude following each refrain. It will be easier to maintain control if you have the children dance while remaining in a circle rather than ranging freely around the room.

Thank You for the Food

Sarah Fletcher, alt.

W. A. Mozart, adapted

Andante graziozo

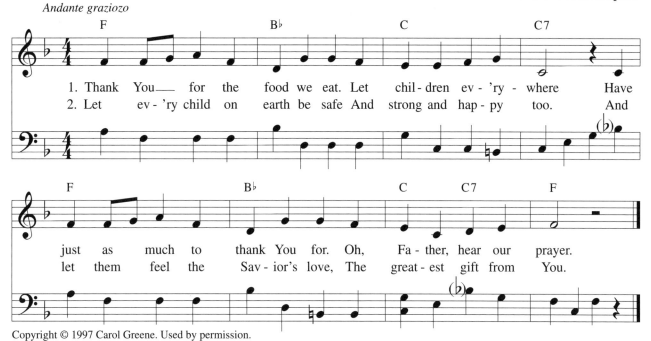

1. Thank You for the food we eat. Let chil-dren ev-'ry-where Have
2. Let ev-'ry child on earth be safe And strong and hap-py too. And

just as much to thank You for. Oh, Fa-ther, hear our prayer.
let them feel the Sav-ior's love, The great-est gift from You.

Show the children pictures of children from various cultures as you teach this song. You might want to have the children prepare snacks representing foods from different cultures. This song also works well as a table-grace or Thanksgiving song.

31

Look, Look, Look at the World

C. G.

Carol Greene

Look, look, look at the world.

Look, look, look at the world.

1. Look at the tu - lips, Danc - ing red tu - lips.
2. Look at the tree - tops, Sway - ing green tree - tops.
3. Look at the a - corns, Bounc - ing brown a - corns.
4. Look at the snow - flakes, Swirl - ing white snow - flakes.

Oh, what a gift from God!

Use this song as you teach about the seasons. Help the children add more stanzas about each season. They will also enjoy waving crepe paper streamers or scarves in appropriate colors as they sing.

32

God So Loved the World

C. G.

Carol Greene

1. God so loved the world. God so loved the world.
2. Je - sus loved the world. Je - sus loved the world.
3. That's why we sing praise. That's why we sing praise.

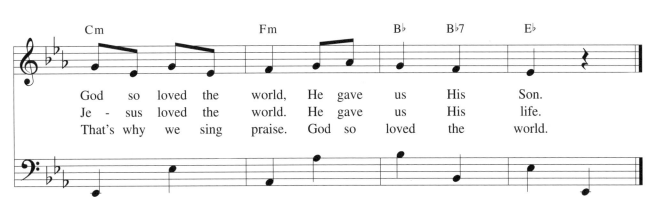

God so loved the world, He gave us His Son.
Je - sus loved the world. He gave us His life.
That's why we sing praise. God so loved the world.

This is a good song to sing at Christmas or Easter—or anytime.

33

Thank You Song

C. G.

Carol Greene

1. We thank You for sun-shine of yel-low and gold. We thank You for moon-light all sil-ver and cold, For crys-tal of star-light and spar-kle of dew. You made them, dear Fa-ther, and so we thank You.

2. We thank You for flow-ers of red, yel-low, blue. We thank You for chil-dren of all col-ors too, For rain-bows that bright-en the whole neigh-bor-hood. You made them, dear Fa-ther, and, oh, they are good!

Have the children name other things God has made that make them happy. They will enjoy dancing and waving colored streamers or scarves as they sing this song.

Sing a Glad Song

C. G.

Carol Greene

Not too fast

1. Fields of flow-ers, for-est trees, Let your song float on the breeze.
2. Gold-en sun and sil-ver moon, Dia-mond stars, shout out a tune.
3. Feath-ered bird and fur-ry beast, From the great-est to the least,

Moun-tains sing and skip like rams, Lit-tle hills like lit-tle lambs.
Sand-y shore and spar-kling sea, Sing a song of praise with me.
Lit-tle child and might-y king, Make the earth with glad-ness ring.

Refrain

Sing a glad song to the Lord, Who has made you with His Word,

Stays be-side you, holds you dear. Lift your voic-es, far and near.

Divide the children into groups to draw a mural of the things described in this song. Point to their drawings as they learn the words. If you sing this song in church, display the children's artwork for the congregation to enjoy.

35

All Things Bright and Beautiful

Cecil Frances Alexander

Richard Roberts

All things bright and beau-ti-ful, all crea-tures great and small,

all things wise and won-der-ful: The Lord God made them all. 1. Each all.
2. He

lit-tle flower that o-pens, each lit-tle bird that sings, He
gave us eyes to see them, and lips that we might tell How

made their glow-ing col-ors, He made their ti-ny wings.
great is God Al-might-y, who has made all things well.

This song also works well as a mural. Help children make up actions for the song as well.

Be Joyful

C. G.

Carol Greene

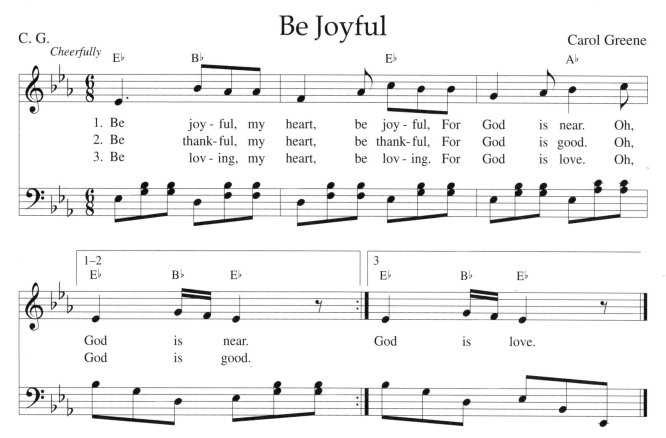

1. Be joy - ful, my heart, be joy - ful, For God is near. Oh,
2. Be thank - ful, my heart, be thank - ful, For God is good. Oh,
3. Be lov - ing, my heart, be lov - ing. For God is love. Oh,

God is near.
God is good.

God is love.

Ask children to tell some of the things they like to do when they're feeling joyful, thankful, and loving.

God Is with Us

C. G.

Carol Greene

38 Help children make up motions for each action in the last phrase—"Love the Lord, help the poor, and rejoice."

Blessings

C. G.

Carol Greene

Happily

1. I am a bless-ing. I am a bless-ing. God made me to be a bless-ing in the world. I am a bless-ing. I am a bless-ing. God made me to bless the whole wide world.

2. You are a bless-ing. You are a bless-ing. God made you to be a bless-ing in the world. You are a bless-ing. You are a bless-ing. God made you to bless the whole wide world.

Help the children think of ways in which they can share Jesus' love and be blessings. Have them point to themselves on the words "I" and "me" and to one another on the word "you."

39

God Bless You, God Bless Me

C. G.

Carol Greene

1. God bless you. God bless me. God bless Bird and
2. God bless you. God bless me. God bless our church

God bless Tree. God bless Rab - bit run - ning free.
fam - i - ly. God bless folks a - cross the sea.

God bless you. God bless me.
God bless you. God bless me.

Cut out magazine pictures or draw simple pictures to illustrate the blessings named in the song. Let children take turns pointing to them as you sing.

40

Love One Another

C. G.

Carol Greene

With movement

F   **C**   **F**

1. Je - sus said, "Love one an - oth - er.
2. Je - sus said, "Love one an - oth - er.

C7   **F**   **F7**

Love as I've al - ways loved you.
Love as I've al - ways loved you.

* B♭   **F**

Love one an - oth - er, Each sis - ter and broth - er. Oh,
Be friends to all,____ To both great and small____ Oh,

C   **C7**   **F**

that's what I want you to do."
that's what I want you to do."

* May be repeated with either or both stanzas.

Ask the children to name members of their families whom they love. (Don't be surprised if they mention pets!) Then help the children name people outside their families that they can befriend.

41

You've Got to Tell

C. G.

Carol Greene

1. When you know Lord Jesus and His love for you, There is just one thing you've simply got to do. You've got to tell, tell, tell, tell, tell. You've got to tell, tell, tell, tell, tell. In a whisper, in a shout, Let it out, let it out! You've got to tell, tell, tell, tell, tell.

2. Jesus' love inside you isn't meant to stay. He's got more for you, so give that love away.

42

Ask the children to march in place during the song, then jump into the air at "Let it out! Let it out!"

Nothing Can Keep Us

C. G.

Carol Greene

Happily

Refrain

Noth-ing can keep us from the love of God. Noth-ing can keep us from the love of God. Big things or small, no, not a thing at all.

Noth-ing can keep us from the love of God.

1. Thun - der and light-ning, scar - y
2. Bad things that oth - er peo - ple

dreams at night, Times when the folks we love are out of sight—
do or say, Dan - gers at home and dan - gers far a - way—

To Refrain

We know that we are go-ing to be all right. Noth-ing can keep us from the love of God.
We know that we are go-ing to be o-kay. Noth-ing can keep us from the love of God.

Encourage the children to talk about examples of the feelings mentioned in the song. Be sensitive to their fears and reinforce the truth that **nothing** can keep us from the love of God.

43

Our Church Is a Family

Carol Greene

Franz Schubert, adapted

Our church is a fam-i-ly, the fam-i-ly of God.

1. We're sis - ters and broth-ers in the fam-i-ly of God.
2. We love one an - oth - er in the fam-i-ly of God.
3. We wel - come all peo - ple in the fam-i-ly of God.

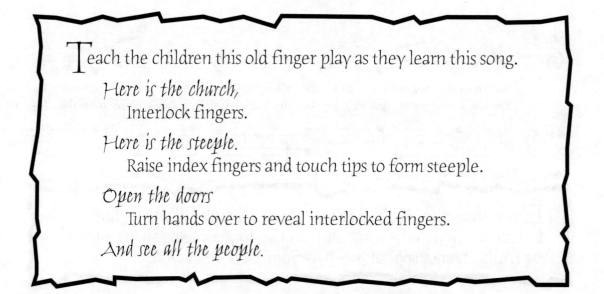

Teach the children this old finger play as they learn this song.

Here is the church,
   Interlock fingers.

Here is the steeple.
   Raise index fingers and touch tips to form steeple.

Open the doors
   Turn hands over to reveal interlocked fingers.

And see all the people.

Don't Mess It Up

C. G.

Carol Greene

Brightly

1. God made the world and it's very, very good.
2. Don't hurt the an-i-mals, don't hurt the trees.

Don't mess it up. Don't mess it up.
Don't mess them up. Don't mess them up.

God made the world and it's ver-y, ver-y good.
Don't hurt the land and don't hurt the seas.

Repeat st. 1 after st. 2.

Don't mess up God's world. No, no, no!
Don't mess up God's world. No, no, no!

Copyright © 1997 Carol Greene. Used by permission.

Cut out magazine pictures to make a poster illustrating this song. Give each child a small paper sack and collect litter as you learn the song.

45

Sheep Ran Away

C. G.

Carol Greene

Moderato

1. Sheep ran a - way, my Lord, my Lord.
2. Folks are like sheep, my Lord, my Lord.

Sheep ran a - way. Oh me, oh my!
Folks are like sheep. Oh me, oh my!

Sheep ran a - way, my Lord, my Lord.
Folks are like sheep, my Lord, my Lord.

Sheep ran a - way. Oh, hear them cry.
Folks are like sheep. Oh, hear them cry.

Refrain

Save those sheep! Save those sheep! Save those sheep, my Lord, my Lord.

Help children learn motions for this song. They might fold their hands for "my Lord"; raise eyebrows for "oh me, oh my"; and wipe their eyes for "hear them cry." They will enjoy beating their open palm with a fist on the words "Save those sheep!"

46

When I Feel Sorry

C. G.

Carol Greene

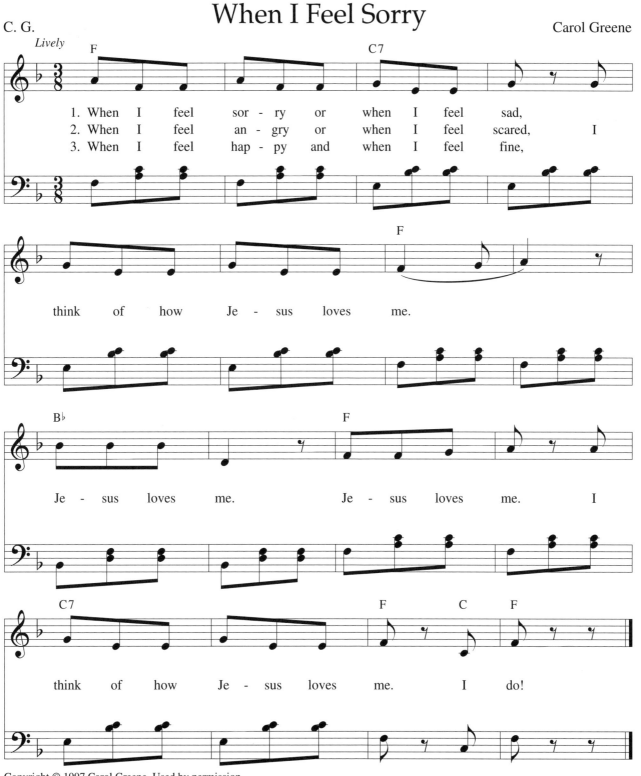

Lively

1. When I feel sor - ry or when I feel sad,
2. When I feel an - gry or when I feel scared, I
3. When I feel hap - py and when I feel fine,

think of how Je - sus loves me.

Je - sus loves me. Je - sus loves me. I

think of how Je - sus loves me. I do!

Encourage the children to talk about times they've experienced each of the feelings expressed in the song. Be careful not to minimize or ridicule any of the feelings. Emphasize the fact that Jesus loves them, no matter what they are feeling.

47

Be Still

C. G.

Carol Greene

1. Be still, be still, be still And let God's lov - ing fill Your trou - bled heart, Ev - 'ry small part. Be still, be still, be still.
2. Be still, be still, be still And know God al - ways will Wipe ev - 'ry tear, Hush ev - 'ry fear. Be still, be still, be still.

48

This song provides another opportunity for the children to talk about their feelings. "When do you cry?" "When are you scared?" Remind them that Jesus helps them in every situation.

Prayer

C. G.

Carol Greene

1. We pray for Your world, Lord. Make war go a-way, And hun-ger and hurt-ing. Oh, bring a new day, A day when all peo-ple will stand hand in hand And peace and pros-per-i-ty shine in each land.
2. We pray for Your world, Lord: The young and the old, The lone-ly, the fright-ened, the lost and the cold. Oh, bring a new day, Lord, when all earth shall know That You hold the whole world and will not let go.

Ask the children, "What things would you change about the world, if you could?" Explain that the word "prosperity" means that everyone has enough of what they need. Suggest simple ways the children can share God's love by serving others.

49

We Are Together

Deborah Carter

We are to-geth-er, we are glad! Be-ing with each oth-er nev-er makes us sad.

We are to-geth-er, we are glad; so let's say "Hi" to _____.

(child's name)

50

Young children love to hear their names sung. Use the "hello" songs to help the children learn one another's names and to welcome new children to the group. You may also want to open and close your choir rehearsal, school day, or music time with these hello and good-bye songs.

Hello, Good Day

C. G.

Carol Greene

Hel - lo, good day, how - dy doo - dle, doo - dle, doo To
you and you and yoo - dle, doo - dle doo. Hel - lo, good day, how - dy
doo - dle, doo - dle, doo To you and you and _____.
(name)

Hello, Everybody

D. C.

Deborah Carter

Hel - lo, ev - 'ry - bod - y! How do you do? How do you do? How do you do?
Hel - lo, ev - 'ry - bod - y! How do you do? God loves _____ to - day.
(child's name)

51

Good-bye, My Friends

C. G.

Carol Greene

Good-bye, So Long, Farewell

D. C.

Deborah Carter

52

Church Year Colors

Deborah Carter

Use this song to teach your children the colors of the church year—Advent: blue; Christmas: white; Epiphany: white; Lent: purple; Easter: white; Pentecost: red. As you begin each season, sing the song with the appropriate color. Have a child pick an item to fill in the stanza. After the children say the item, have them pat their legs, then clap. It is fun to make this a cumulative song, listing seven or eight items, patting and clapping after each item.

Copy the chart on the next page and display it in your room. Color the appropriate section of the circle as you begin each season. You may want to give each child a copy of the circle to display at home too. As you introduce each season, give each child a shape (candle: blue; manger: white; star: white; cross: purple; empty tomb or butterfly: white; dove: red) cut from the appropriate color of construction paper. Challenge the children to find that color in church on Sunday.

The Colors of the Church Year

54

Waiting in Advent

D. C.

Deborah Carter

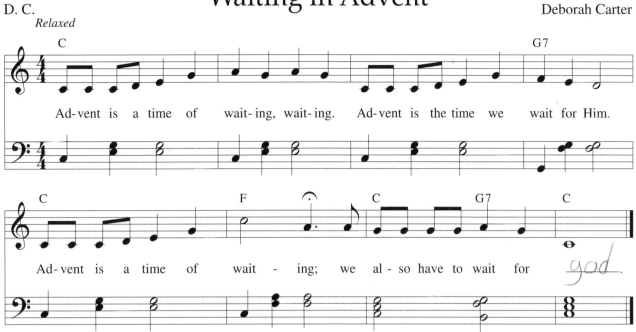

Ad-vent is a time of wait-ing, wait-ing. Ad-vent is the time we wait for Him.

Ad-vent is a time of wait - ing; we al-so have to wait for god.

Children will enjoy adding things they have to wait for at the end of the song—birthdays, summer vacations, etc. Have fun with the fermata—make them wait!

55

Christmas Gift Song

D. C.

Deborah Carter

AT Tyler *(Child's name)* got a **car** *(item)* as a Christ-mas gift.

Thank You, Lord, for giv-ing us such great, great gifts!

× = clap

This is a good song to use on your first meeting after Christmas. Pair up the children and have them clap their hands against their partner's hands at the ×'s.

Valentine's Day Is about Love

D. C.

Deborah Carter

With a lilt

We show our love by **god** Val-en-tine's Day is a-bout love.

Lov-ing, lov-ing. Val-en-tine's Day is a-bout love.

56

Ask children to think of ways in which they can share Jesus' love by being loving to others. Enlarge the puzzle on the next page and let children take turns circling the quarter notes to find a hidden picture. Or, you may want to give each child a copy of the puzzle.

My Valentine's Puzzle

Use a red crayon or marker to circle each quarter note. What did you find?

Thanksgiving Song

Deborah Carter

D. C.

Seriously

Thanks - giv - ing Day is com - ing. Thank God for our bless - ings. Thank God for our _____.

cresc. Yeah!

Ask children to suggest what they're thankful for at the blank. During the measures of whole rests, have children hit palms on floor (while sitting on the floor; stamp one foot if standing) at beat 1 and clap on beats 2-3-4, getting progressively louder until they shout "Yeah!"

Songs and Activities that Teach Music Theory

Whole Note

o

ta—a—a—a

Half Note

ta—a

Quarter Note

ta

Eighth Notes

ta—ti

59

Rhythm Chant

These are whole notes:

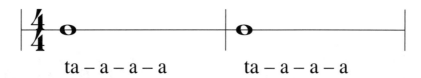

ta – a – a – a   ta – a – a – a

These are half notes:

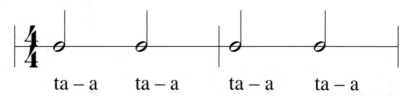

ta – a   ta – a   ta – a   ta – a

These are quarter notes:

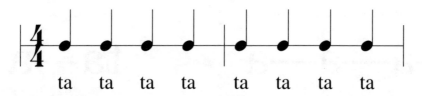

ta ta ta ta ta ta ta ta

These are eighth notes:

ta- ti ta- ti ta- ti ta- ti   ta- ti ta- ti ta- ti ta- ti Pow!

Copy the note cards on the previous page and teach the children the names of each note and the syllable chant for its value. Show children a familiar hymnal, songbook, or song chart and let them find similar notes. When the children have learned all the notes, enlarge this rhythm chant. First, have the children clap the rhythm. Then have them say the spoken lines in a quarter-note rhythm. Children will enjoy doing a huge crescendo (teach that word and sign) on the eighth notes and shouting "Pow!" at the end.

60

Catch-the-Rhythm Fish

Enlarge this page and display the chart. Play or clap a rhythm and let children identify the matching fish. You may also want to give each child a copy of the page and have them point to (or color) the correct fish.

61

Alphabet Chant

Enlarge this chart and display it in your room. Teach the first two phrases thoroughly before teaching the whole chant. Once the children know the chant, help them establish a rhythm—hit palms on floor for beat 1, clap for beat 2—and continue the rhythm throughout the chant.

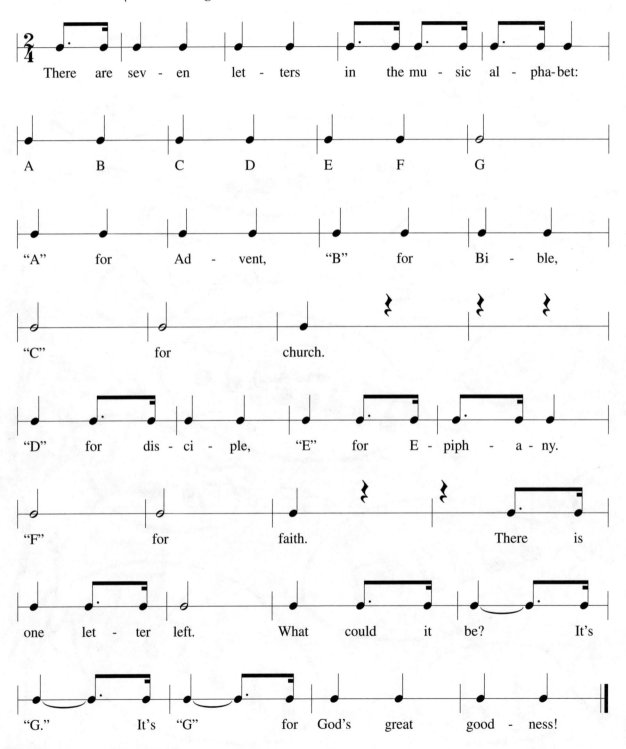

The Music Alphabet

After your children have learned the alphabet chant, enlarge this chart and display it. Beginning with the ascending alphabet, say a phrase of the chant and have a child point to the correct letter. Then say the phrases for the descending alphabet. You may want to give each child a copy of the page and have them point to, or color, the letter for each phrase.

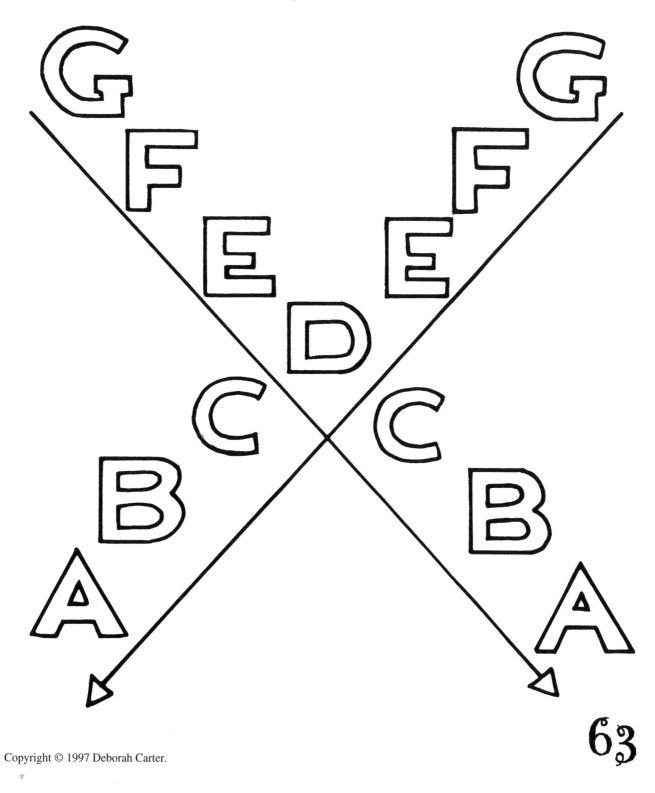

63

Alphabet Animals

Copy this page for each child. Call out a letter from the musical alphabet and have the children point to, or color, the animal whose name starts with that letter.

BEAR

CAT

DOG

ANT

GIRAFFE

ELEPHANT

FISH

64

The LOUD and Soft Song

Carol Greene

Deborah Carter

The li-on goes "ROAR," the kit-ten goes "meow."

SPLASH goes the storm, drip goes the dew. The cym-bal goes

CRASH, the flute goes toot. Tap goes the slip-per,

CLOMP goes the boot. "Goo," says the ba-by, "RAH," says the

crowd. Thank You, God, for soft and LOUD.

Enlarge or draw the chart on the next page to help you teach this song. Explain that in music, *p* means *piano* or soft; *f* means *forte* or loud. Help the children sing the song with correct dynamics. Expect some giggles at the end!

The LOUD and Soft Song Chart

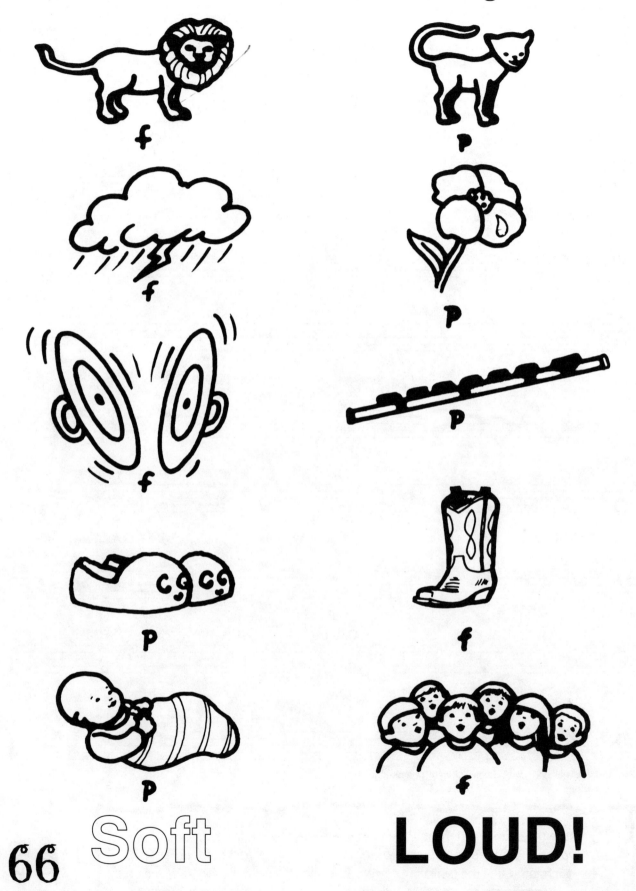

66 Soft   LOUD!

Listening for LOUD and Soft

Enlarge this page or make a copy for each child. Play or sing notes loudly and quietly. On each note have the children point to, or circle, something that makes a quiet or loud noise. This activity helps train a child's ear to differentiate between loud and soft tones.

67

Forte and Piano

Enlarge this page for the children to color together as they arrive, or make a copy for each child. Explain that they may color the shapes with *forte* signs with different colors, but all the shapes with *piano* signs should be colored yellow. They will find a hidden picture if they do it correctly.

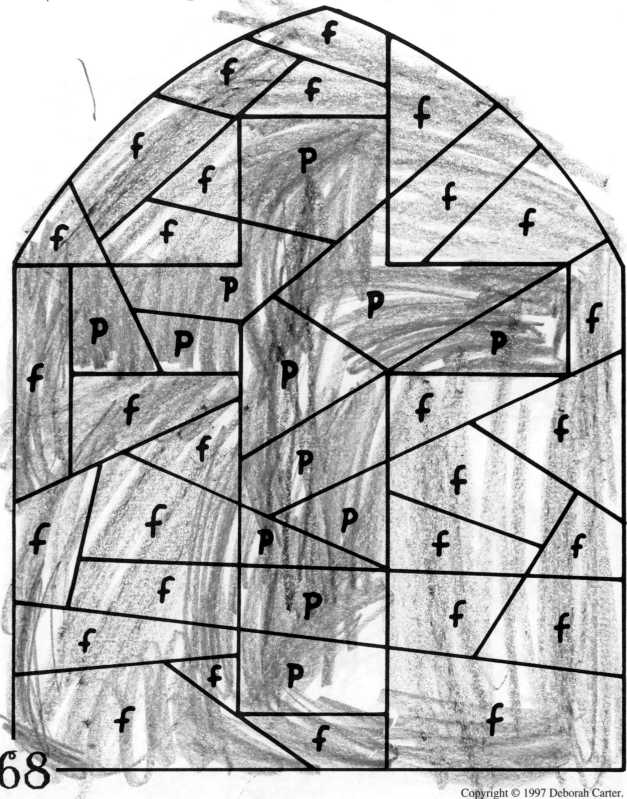

68

The High-Low Song

Deborah Carter

God made the heav'ns, God made the earth. God made it all be - fore my birth.

Heav'n's up high, earth's be - low. High notes, low notes, here we go!

This song helps the children hear the difference between high and low notes. Have the children stand up on measures 1 and 5. Have them sit down on measures 2 and 6. On measure 7 have them stand up on beats 1 and 2 and sit down on beats 3 and 4.

High Notes and Low Notes

Enlarge this page or make a copy for each child. Sing or play high notes and low notes. As you play each note, have the children match it with something that can go high in the air or that will stay low on the ground.

70

Treble Clef and Bass Clef

Copy these cards and teach the children to recognize the treble clef and bass clef. Explain that the treble clef indicates high notes and the bass clef low notes. Let the children find these signs in familiar hymnals and songbooks.

The High-Low Christmas Tree

After teaching the children to recognize the treble and bass clef signs, enlarge this page or make a copy for each child. Ask the children to point to, or color, an ornament with a treble clef when you play or sing a high note, and a bass clef when you sing or play a low note.

72

Mr. Music

Before teaching this song, teach the children what a quarter rest looks like. Enlarge the Mr. Music chart or make a copy for each child. As you sing each stanza, let the children trace the appropriate part of Mr. Music. Note that in the song the fictional name *Dwar* rhymes with star.

Mr. Music's Song

D. C.

Deborah Carter

There was a man who lived on Dwar. Dwar is
out a - mongst the stars. There was a man who
lived on Dwar and his name was Mis - ter Mu - sic. 1. His

(1.) head	looked	just	like	a	half	note,	half
(2.) bod - y	looked	just	like	a	whole	note,	whole
(3.) legs	looked	just	like	two	quar - ter	notes,	quar - ter
(4.) eyes	looked	just	like	two	eighth	notes,	eighth
(5.) arms	looked	just	like	two	half	notes,	half
(6.) mouth	looked	just	like	a	quar - ter	rest,	quar - ter
(7.) ears	looked	just	like	two	bass	clefs,	bass
(8.) hair	looked	just	like	some	half	notes,	half
(9.) but - tons	looked	just	like	some	tre - ble	clefs,	tre - ble

74

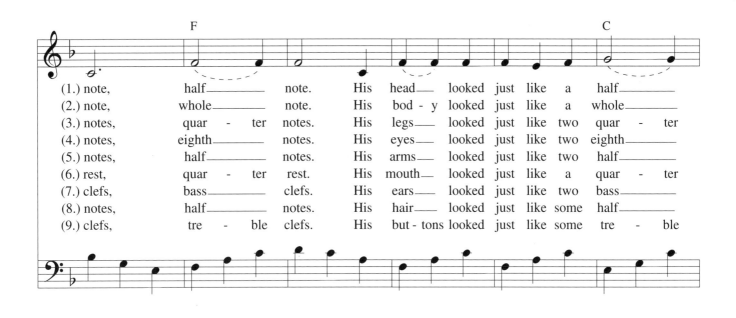

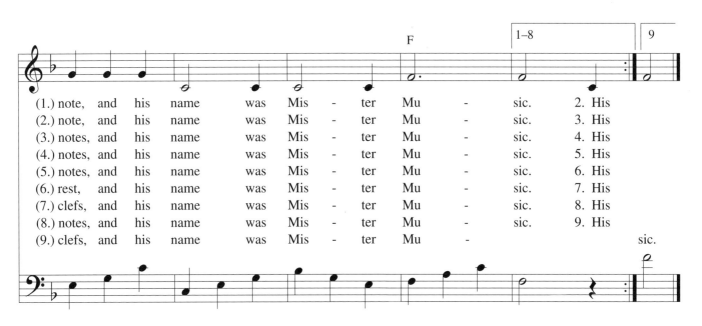

75

God's Little Beetle

Deborah Carter

D. C.

This song will provide an active break during music time and stimulate the children's imaginations. You will definitely want to follow it with a quiet song!

God's Little Beetle

1

Have children point to one of their fingers as if the beetle is sitting there.

2
There's a little, tiny beetle, God's little beetle,
A little, tiny beetle in the air.
A little, tiny beetle, God's little beetle,
Whoops! I see him on that chair.

Children pretend to see the beetle flying around the room and landing on a chair.

3
There's a little, tiny beetle, God's little beetle,
A little, tiny beetle on that chair.
A little, tiny beetle, God's little beetle,
Whoops! He flew into the air.

Children point at the beetle on the chair, then point to him flying around the room again.

4
There's a little, tiny beetle, God's little beetle,
A little, tiny beetle in the air.
A little, tiny beetle, God's little beetle,
Whoops! I see him in (child's name)'s hair!

Children pretend the beetle is flying, then landing in someone's hair.

5
There's a little, tiny beetle, God's little beetle,
A little, tiny beetle in (child's name)'s hair!
A little, tiny beetle, God's little beetle,
Whoops! He flew into the air.

Children point to the beetle in someone's hair, then pretend he is flying around the room again.

6
There's a little, tiny beetle, God's little beetle,
A little, tiny beetle in the air.
A little, tiny beetle, God's little beetle,
How he lives without a care.

Children pretend the beetle is flying. Have them clap the rests in the final ending.

77

Happy, Happy, Happy Birthday

C. G.

Carol Greene

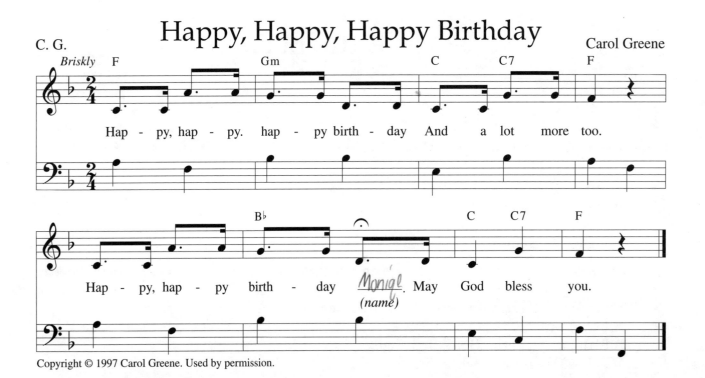

Hap - py, hap - py, hap - py birth - day And a lot more too.

Hap - py, hap - py birth - day *Monique*. May God bless you.

(name)

Copyright © 1997 Carol Greene. Used by permission.

Sing this song for children's birthdays. There is plenty of room to add more than one name at the fermata if you need to. Remember to celebrate birthdays of children which fall on the days you don't meet. Copy the birthday card to give to children with birthdays.

78

Seasonal Index

The following songs are particularly suitable for seasonal use during the church year.

Advent

Christmas

Epiphany

Lent

Palm Sunday

Easter

Pentecost

Thanksgiving

Title Index